FEARON'S
American Literature
WORKBOOK

GLOBE FEARON EDUCATIONAL PUBLISHER
A Division of Simon & Schuster
Upper Saddle River, New Jersey

Fearon's Pacemaker Curriculum Workbooks

Executive Editor: Joan Carrafiello
Project Editor: Carol Schneider
Editor: Renée E. Beach
Product Development: Pencil Point Studio
Production: Pencil Point Studio
Marketing Manager: Margaret Rakus
Cover Design: Pat Smythe
Cover Photograph: Farrell Greyhan/Photo Researchers

ISBN 0-8359-1384-8

Printed in the United States of America

10 9 8 7   99 00

 GLOBE FEARON EDUCATIONAL PUBLISHER
A Division of Simon & Schuster
Upper Saddle River, New Jersey

Table of Contents

Unit 6: Family

Chapter 14

Childtimes	Exercise 1: Analysis
Childtimes	Exercise 2: Synthesis
The Medicine Bag	Exercise 1: Analysis
The Medicine Bag	Exercise 2: Application
Abuela	Exercise 1: Synthesis
Abuela	Exercise 2: Application

Chapter 15

I Ask My Mother To Sing	Exercise 1: Application
Mother to Son	Exercise 1: Synthesis
My Father's Song	Exercise 1: Evaluation
Lineage	Exercise 1: Evaluation
Abuela	Exercise 1: Application
Grandma Ling	Exercise 1: Synthesis
Grandma Ling	Exercise 2: Evaluation
Aunt Sue's Stories	Exercise 1: Synthesis
Bailando	Exercise 1: Application
To My Dear and Loving Husband	Exercise 1: Evaluation

Unit 7: Adventure

Chapter 16

Escape: A Slave Narrative	Exercise 1: Application
Escape: A Slave Narrative	Exercise 2: Synthesis
At Last I Kill a Buffalo	Exercise 1: Analysis
At Last I Kill a Buffalo	Exercise 2: Synthesis

Chapter 17

The Secret Life of Walter Mitty	Exercise 1: Evaluation
The Secret Life of Walter Mitty	Exercise 2: Analysis
The Invalid's Story	Exercise 1: Analysis
The Invalid's Story	Exercise 2: Evaluation

What is Critical Thinking?

Critical thinking—or, to put it another way, thinking critically—means putting information to use. Imagine that you are in a supermarket. You want to buy a can of soup, but you are uncertain which brand to choose. As you read the ingredients listed on the label, you review the number of calories in each serving. Perhaps you check the vitamin and fat content. You may also look at the price listed on the shelf. Then you *evaluate* the information and make a choice. You have just used your critical thinking skills. Critical thinking is the act of processing information and using it in a meaningful way.

The activities in this workbook go along with your Fearon American Literature textbook. They are designed to challenge your critical thinking skills. You will be asked to use four different types of critical thinking skills—all of which you use every day.

Some of the activities in this workbook are labeled *Application*. These activities ask you to put information to use by solving a problem or completing a task. For example, imagine you have just read a story about a boy lost in the wilderness. You might be asked to *apply* what you have just read by writing what you would do if you were the lost boy.

You will find other activities labeled *Analysis*. These activities ask you to look closely at a body of information and to examine all of its parts. You might be asked to *analyze* a character by answering questions about his or her thoughts, feelings, and actions.

Some workbook activities fall under the heading of *Synthesis*. In these activities you will be combining pieces of information to make a whole. You might create a time line of story events, or you might *synthesize* pieces of information in a diary entry.

You will also find activities labeled *Evaluation*. These exercises ask you to make a judgement about certain information. For example, you might read a statement and decide if it is a fact or an opinion. Remember the supermarket described at the beginning of this page? As a shopper, you were *evaluating* information listed on the soup can label.

Your textbook is a wonderful source of knowledge. By studying it, you will learn a great deal of information about American Literature. But the real value of that information will come when you know how to put it to use by thinking critically.

Exercise 1 Application   La Llorona: The Weeping Woman

Name _____ Date _____

**List the three events that led María to throw her children in the river.
Write the events on the lines.**

1 _____

    _____

    _____

2 _____

    _____

    _____

3 _____

    _____

    _____

Exercise 2 Synthesis   La Llorona: The Weeping Woman

Name _____ Date _____

Pretend you grew up in María's village. As a child, you were told the story of the weeping woman. Will you tell your children the story someday? Why or why not?

_____

_____

_____

_____

_____

_____

_____

_____

_____

_____

_____

_____

_____

_____

_____

_____

_____

_____

_____

Exercise 1 Analysis   The Tell-Tale Heart

Name _____ Date _____

Circle *true* **or** *false* **for each statement. If false, write the correct statement on the lines below.**

1. A police officer is telling the story.   TRUE   FALSE

   _____

   _____

   _____

2. The neighbors heard the old man's cries.   TRUE   FALSE

   _____

   _____

   _____

3. The police officer heard the old man's heartbeat.   TRUE   FALSE

   _____

   _____

   _____

4. The narrator was bothered by the old man's eye.   TRUE   FALSE

   _____

   _____

   _____

5. The narrator believes he is not mad.   TRUE   FALSE

   _____

   _____

   _____

6. The old man's body was hidden behind a wall.   TRUE   FALSE

   _____

   _____

   _____

Exercise 2 Evaluation   The Tell-Tale Heart

Name _____ Date _____

**As he tells the story, the narrator insists he is not mad. Do you agree?
Why or why not? Write your answer in the space below.**

I know the narrator _____ mad because:
(is / is not)

_____

_____

_____

_____

_____

_____

_____

_____

Now make a list of reasons to support your decision.

_____

_____

_____

_____

_____

_____

_____

_____

_____

Exercise 1 Application   The Pepper Tree

Name _____ Date _____

Fill in the blanks. Use your answers to complete the puzzle.

1. The old man sees a _____ in his room.

2. The ghost repeats the words "___ _____ _____!"

3. The ghost pointed the old man towards the _____ _____.

4. When the ghost threw off his shroud, the old man saw the _____ _____.

5. The Bald One was the symbol of _____.

6. "Don't let _____ be your guide."

Exercise 2 Evaluation   The Pepper Tree

Name _____ Date _____

Pretend you are a newspaper reporter. Write a review of "The Pepper Tree." Be sure to summarize the story and tell whether people should or should not read it.

FEARON DAILY NEWS

_____   _____
_____   _____
_____   _____
_____   _____
_____   _____
_____   _____
_____   _____
_____   _____
_____   _____
_____   _____
_____   _____
_____   _____
_____   _____
_____   _____
_____   _____

Exercise 1 Analysis   The Raven

Name _____ Date _____

Imagine that you are the narrator. You are writing a letter to your lost love, Lenore. Describe how the raven's visit made you feel that evening.

My Dearest Lenore,

_____

_____

_____

_____

_____

_____

_____

_____

_____

_____

_____

_____

_____

_____

_____

_____

_____

Exercise 2 Analysis   The Raven

Name _____ Date _____

A. **The way the author feels about a subject is felt in the *tone* of the story or poem. In "The Raven," Poe uses different tones of voice to let us know how the narrator feels the night he sees the raven. Discuss his use of tone by answering the following questions.**

   1. Whenever the narrator mentions the name Lenore, how do you think his voice sounds? Sad? Angry? Loud? Happy? Choose one answer and tell why you made that choice.

   _____

   _____

   _____

   _____

   2. Reread the last stanza of the poem. How do you think the narrator feels as he says the last two lines? Very tired? Relieved? Extremely unhappy? Silly? Choose one answer and tell why you made your choice.

   _____

   _____

   _____

   _____

   3. When the poem begins, the narrator hears the tapping at his door. He says to himself, "Tis some visitor," I muttered, "tapping at my chamber door." If you were reading this stanza aloud, how would you read it? Loudly? Quickly? As if you were very tired? As if you were very happy? Choose one answer and tell why you made your choice.

   _____

   _____

   _____

   _____

B. **After you have read the poem several times, try to read it aloud. It will take a little practice before you feel comfortable. Use different tones of voice to express the way the narrator feels throughout the poem. Practice your reading before the class.**

Exercise 1 Analysis   The Cremation of Sam McGee

Name _____ Date _____

Circle *true* or *false* for each statement. If false, write the correct statement on the lines below.

1. Sam McGee liked the cold weather.   TRUE   FALSE

   _____

   _____

   _____

2. The poet promised to bury Sam McGee.   TRUE   FALSE

   _____

   _____

   _____

3. The poet wanted to carry Sam on his sled.   TRUE   FALSE

   _____

   _____

   _____

4. Sam didn't want to be buried in a cold grave.   TRUE   FALSE

   _____

   _____

   _____

5. The poet found a cottage and made it a crematorium.   TRUE   FALSE

   _____

   _____

   _____

6. Sam was happy to be cremated because he was finally warm.   TRUE   FALSE

   _____

   _____

   _____

Exercise 2 Application   **The Cremation of Sam McGee**

Name _____ Date _____

A. Pretend you are a travel agent. You have the assignment of trying to persuade people who like adventure to consider visiting the area described in the poem—northern Canada. Use the poem to gather the following information.

Weather (What is it like? Is it ever sunny? Explain.)

_____

_____

_____

Transportation (HINT: How would people travel?)

_____

_____

_____

People (Are they friendly? Are they loyal? Explain. HINT: Use the characters from the poem.)

_____

_____

_____

Trails (Name at least one which travelers could use.)

_____

_____

_____

B. Use the information you have just gathered. Write a brief advertisement for this area. Your travel ad should be short. You must be able to convince customers to go there by your description. Use the back of this sheet to write your ad.

Exercise 1 Application   Hist, Whist

Name _____ Date _____

A. **List the words and phrases the poet uses to describe each character.**

Witch

_____
_____
_____
_____
_____
_____

Toad

_____
_____
_____
_____
_____
_____

Mouse

_____
_____
_____
_____
_____
_____

Devil

_____
_____
_____
_____
_____
_____

B. **Pretend you are a poet. You decide to add another "little ghostthing" to the poem. Use the back of this sheet to list words and phrases that describe the new character you will add.**

Exercise 1 Analysis   Dust Tracks on a Road

Name _____ Date _____

Create a story map by answering the questions. Begin your answers at the SETTING marker.

CLIMAX
What happened when the narrator read her part of the story in class?

_____

_____

_____

PLOT EVENTS
When the two women came, were the teacher and narrator prepared for the visit?

_____

_____

_____

PLOT EVENTS
Why did the narrator go to the Park House hotel?

_____

_____

_____

PLOT EVENTS
What were the students usually told to do before visitors came to school?

_____

_____

_____

PLOT EVENTS
What did the narrator receive from the women?

_____

_____

_____

CHARACTER
Who are the important people in the story?

_____

_____

_____

END
How did the narrator feel at the end of the story?

_____

_____

_____

SETTING
Where does this story take place?

_____

_____

_____

Exercise 2 Application

Dust Tracks on a Road

Name _____ Date _____

Pretend you are one of the other students in Mr. Calhoun's class. At dinner that evening, you discuss your day at school with your family. Describe your conversation about the two women who came to visit your class.

_____

_____

_____

_____

_____

_____

_____

_____

_____

_____

_____

_____

_____

_____

_____

_____

_____

_____

_____

_____

Exercise 1 Analysis   Lame Deer Remembers His Childhood

Name _____ Date _____

The life of the Ikce Wicasa (the natural humans) was very different from your life. On the lines below, compare your own experiences with those of the narrator. The first one has been done for you.

Lame Deer   Me

born in a log cabin   *born in a hospital*

_____   _____

_____   _____

_____   _____

_____   _____

_____   _____

_____   _____

_____   _____

_____   _____

_____   _____

_____   _____

_____   _____

_____   _____

_____   _____

Exercise 2 Application   Lame Deer Remembers His Childhood

Name _____ Date _____

A. At the end of the story, Lame Deer's father gave him a white stallion.
What would you do if you were Lame Deer's father? Why? Write your
answer in the space below.

_____

_____

_____

_____

_____

_____

_____

_____

B. Now pretend that you are Lame Deer. You have just heard why your father
gave you the white stallion. How do you feel about receiving it? Write
your answer in the space below.

_____

_____

_____

_____

_____

_____

_____

_____

Exercise 1 Analysis   Prisoner of My Country

Name _____ Date _____

A. A *fact* is something that is known for sure and without question.
An *opinion* is based on what a person thinks. Read each quotation
from the story. Decide if it is a fact or an opinion. Put a check in the
correct column.

		FACT	OPINION
1.	"The church was a Civil Control Station, where we were supposed to report."	❑	❑
2.	"But the army didn't seem to care if we worried or not. To them, we were only prisoners."	❑	❑
3.	"Some people were crying quietly, but most of us were silent."	❑	❑
4.	"Being here was not only degrading, it did not seem real. It was like an awful dream."	❑	❑
5.	"But dinner was a piece of bread, a boiled potato and two sausages from a can."	❑	❑
6.	"They would have given us no support if we had tried to stop the army from taking us away."	❑	❑

B. Review the quotations above. Choose one which you have marked as an
opinion. Do you agree with this opinion? Why or why not? Write your
answer in the space below.

_____

_____

_____

_____

_____

_____

_____

Exercise 2 Synthesis

Prisoner of My Country

Name _____ Date _____

Imagine that you are Yoshiko Uchida. You have just spent your first week at the Japanese-American internment camp. Write a letter to the President of the United States. Tell him what it is like being there and how you feel about it.

Dear Mr. President,

_____

_____

_____

_____

_____

_____

_____

_____

_____

_____

_____

_____

_____

_____

_____

_____

_____

Sincerely,
Yoshiko Uchida

Exercise 1 Evaluation

The Circuit

Name _____ Date _____

A. You have just read a story about a young migrant farm worker. Do you think children should be allowed to work the fields in the same way the narrator did? Put a check next to the statements that support your opinion.

_____   **1.** Young children should work as hard as adults.

_____   **2.** Children should go to school all the time, not just when there is no work available.

_____   **3.** If a family needs money to survive, everyone must work.

_____   **4.** Working the fields is a good education, even if it is not school work.

_____   **5.** Children cannot handle the responsibility of supporting a family.

_____   **6.** Traveling to different places to find work is exciting.

_____   **7.** Working with your whole family creates stronger, happier relationships.

_____   **8.** Children should be allowed to play and have fun instead of working.

B. Write a short paragraph defending your opinion. Be sure to describe how you feel about children working in the fields. Give reasons why you feel this way.

_____

_____

_____

_____

_____

_____

_____

_____

_____

_____

Exercise 2 Application   The Circuit

Name _____ Date _____

A. When Panchito returns home from school, he is excited. He wants to tell his family about the trumpet lessons. Instead, he sees the boxes ready for packing. Complete the story by writing what happened after the boxes were packed.

_____

_____

_____

_____

_____

_____

_____

_____

_____

_____

_____

_____

B. Now change the ending by writing what you would *like* to happen when Panchito returns from school. Use the back of this sheet if you need more space.

_____

_____

_____

_____

_____

_____

_____

_____

Exercise 1 Analysis   The Jacket

Name _____ Date _____

When the author's mother buys him a new jacket, he is not very happy about it. In the space below, list the words and phrases the author uses to describe the new jacket.

Exercise 2 Application   **The Jacket**

Name _____ Date _____

A. Did anyone ever give or buy you a piece of clothing that you hated?
Describe that piece of clothing in the space below.

_____

_____

_____

_____

_____

_____

_____

B. Use your description to draw
the piece of clothing.
Draw it on the hanger.

Exercise 1 Analysis

The Ballad of John Henry

Name _____ Date _____

A. A *fact* is something that is known for sure and without question. An *opinion* is based on what a person thinks. Read each statement below. Put a check in the correct column.

		FACT	OPINION
1.	John Henry always wanted to be a "steel drivin' man."	❏	❏
2.	The steam drill was definitely the best way to drive steel bits into the rock.	❏	❏
3.	John Henry is the greatest folk hero.	❏	❏
4.	There was a contest between the steam drill and John Henry.	❏	❏
5.	John Henry died of a broken heart.	❏	❏

B. List three reasons explaining why you think John Henry became a folk hero.

_____

_____

_____

_____

_____

_____

_____

_____

Exercise 1 Analysis   Harriet Tubman

Name _____ Date _____

Circle *true* or *false* for each statement. If false, write the correct statement on the lines below.

1. Harriet Tubman was a slave at one time.   TRUE   FALSE

   _____

   _____

   _____

2. Harriet was freed from slavery by her slave owner.   TRUE   FALSE

   _____

   _____

   _____

3. The slave catchers caught Harriet in the North.   TRUE   FALSE

   _____

   _____

   _____

4. Harriet Tubman freed nineteen other slaves.   TRUE   FALSE

   _____

   _____

   _____

5. Harriet Tubman was not afraid of the slave catchers.   TRUE   FALSE

   _____

   _____

   _____

6. Harriet Tubman was captured.   TRUE   FALSE

   _____

   _____

   _____

Exercise 1 Analysis   A Chant of Darkness

Name _____ Date _____

A. The following quotations are from the poem. Choose the correct word from the list below to fill in each blank.

fingers   life   light   love   darkness   rest   night

1. "In blank _____ I stumbled."

2. "The torch that is the _____ unto my feet."

3. "The words of _____ set my spirit aflame."

4. "My eager _____ searched out the mysteries."

5. "The ecstasy of _____ is abroad in the world."

6. "O wide, spacious _____ , I love thee!"

7. "Like a dove, I _____ in thy bosom."

B. Using the words you found, plus your own words, write about what Helen Keller was thinking when she wrote this poem.

_____

_____

_____

_____

_____

_____

_____

_____

_____

_____

_____

Exercise 1 Analysis   The Unsung Heroes

Name _____ Date _____

A. **The main characters of the poem are the unsung heroes. Write words that describe the unsung heroes on the lines below.**

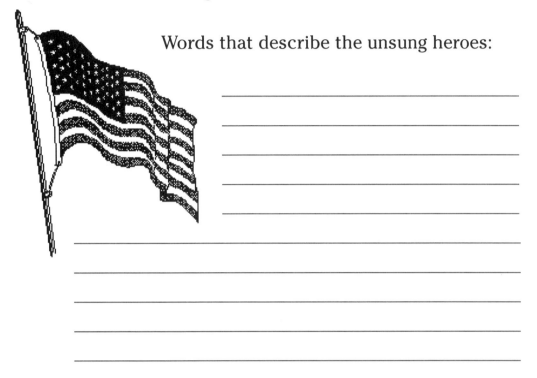

Words that describe the unsung heroes:

_____

_____

_____

_____

_____

_____

_____

_____

_____

_____

B. **A monument (a statue which honors a person or event) is being built in your community. The committee you are on would like to have the monument honor unsung heroes. Write a short speech telling why you think this monument should be built. Include your list of words in your speech. Use the back of this page if you need more space.**

_____

_____

_____

_____

_____

_____

_____

_____

Exercise 1 Application   Paul Revere's Ride

Name _____ Date _____

Think of what you know about the poem, "Paul Revere's Ride." Use this information to write the MAIN IDEA of the poem in the first box. Then write DETAILS that support the main idea in the boxes below.

MAIN IDEA

DETAILS   DETAILS   DETAILS

Exercise 1 Synthesis   Behind the Waterfall

Name _____ Date _____

Put the events in order by numbering them 1-10.

Buffalo began to come out of the hill.	☐

☐	Sweet Medicine and Standing On The Ground bathed in the stream.

The old woman offered the men corn and buffalo meat.	☐

☐	The two men climbed to the top of the hill.

The two Cheyenne men went behind the waterfall.	☐

☐	The old woman painted the young men.

The young men brought food to the camp.	☐

☐	The Cheyenne began to hunt the buffalo.

The people ate the food.	☐

☐	The Cheyenne planted corn in the spring.

Exercise 2 Application   Behind the Waterfall

Name _____ Date _____

Create a story map by filling in the boxes and blanks below.

TITLE: _____

SETTING:
Where does the story take place?

CHARACTERS:
Who are the main people in the story?   _____

_____

_____

PROBLEM:
What is the main problem in the
story that needs to be resolved?

EVENTS:
What are some of the
events that lead to solving
the problem?

EVENT 1: _____
_____

EVENT 2: _____
_____

EVENT 3: _____
_____

EVENT 4: _____
_____

SOLUTION:
How is the problem solved?

Fearon's American Literature Workbook

Exercise 1 Application Paul Bunyan, the Mightiest Logger of Them All

Name _____ Date _____

You read about all the places Paul Bunyan had been and all of the things he did. Using the map below, draw a line from the event to the place where it happened.

BORN   CREATED THE GREAT LAKES   CREATED THE GRAND CANYON

CUT PINE, SPRUCE, AND RED WILLOW

Exercise 2 Application   Paul Bunyan, the Mightiest Logger of Them All

Name _____ Date _____

Paul Bunyan cut down trees to clear the land. He did this at a time when there were many forests. People started towns and cities on the cleared land.

Now, the rain forests, which fill only seven percent of the earth, are being destroyed. This will be very harmful to life on earth as we know it. Already, almost half of the world's rain forests have been destroyed. Land, trees, wildlife, and plants we use as medicine have been lost and cannot be replaced.

Do you think Paul Bunyan would be concerned about saving the rain forests? Why or why not? Write a letter he might send to the editor of his local newspaper describing how he feels about the rain forests.

Dear Editor,

_____

_____

_____

_____

_____

_____

_____

_____

_____

_____

_____

_____

_____

Very truly yours,
Paul Bunyan

Exercise 1 Analysis   Thank You, M'am

Name _____ Date _____

An author lets the reader understand characters by describing their actions and feelings. Use the chart below to produce your "word picture" of Mrs. Luella Bates Washington Jones.

In the box marked "Characteristic," write a word to describe Mrs. Jones. Then, in the box marked "Example," write about a part of the story or write a quotation from Mrs. Jones to support your conclusion. The first one has been done for you.

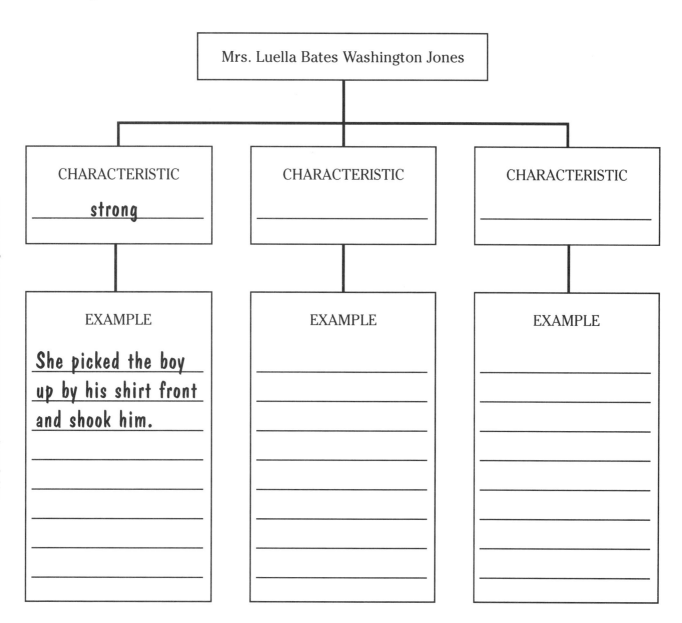

Mrs. Luella Bates Washington Jones

CHARACTERISTIC	CHARACTERISTIC	CHARACTERISTIC
strong		

EXAMPLE	EXAMPLE	EXAMPLE
She picked the boy up by his shirt front and shook him.		

Exercise 2 Application   **Thank You, M'am**

Name _____ Date _____

In the story, the woman tells the boy, "You ought to be my son. I would teach you right from wrong." Pretend that the boy *is* her son. Write a paragraph describing what Mrs. Jones would teach the boy.

_____

_____

_____

_____

_____

_____

_____

_____

_____

_____

_____

_____

_____

_____

_____

_____

_____

Exercise 1 Synthesis   Rosa Parks

Name _____ Date _____

What do you already know about Rosa Parks? What do you want to know more about? What have you learned by reading the story? Complete the chart by filling in the columns.

1. In the first column, fill in what you already know about the rights of African Americans in the 1950's.

2. In the second column, fill in what you want to know about Rosa Parks and the beginning of the civil rights movement in the 1950's.

3. After you have read the story, fill in the final column with what you have learned about Rosa Parks and the civil rights movement.

Part of the first column is done for you.

What Do I Know?	What Do I Want to Know?	What Have I Learned?
African Americans were treated unfairly.		

Exercise 2 Application   Rosa Parks

Name _____ Date _____

Rosa Parks was a brave woman. She stood up for her rights, and didn't give up, even when it was difficult. Have you ever had to stand up for something you believe in? Describe what you stood up for. What happened as a result of your actions?

_____

_____

_____

_____

_____

_____

_____

_____

_____

_____

_____

_____

_____

_____

_____

_____

_____

_____

Exercise 1 Analysis   Roberto Clemente: A Bittersweet Memoir

Name _____ Date _____

A. Write the name of the main character in the baseball. Then write words describing the character on the blank lines around the ball.

_____   _____

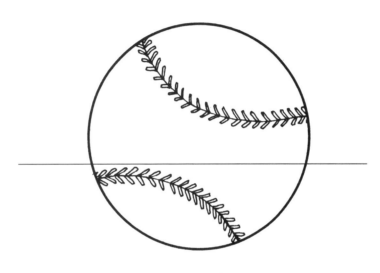

_____   _____

B. In the story, Clemente insists on traveling to Nicaragua, even though it was New Year's Eve and he knew there had been a problem with the airplane. Why do you think he made the decision to take the trip? Before you write your answer, review your list of words describing Clemente's character. Try to use some of these words in your answer. Use the back of this sheet to write.

Exercise 2 Synthesis   Roberto Clemente: A Bittersweet Memoir

Name _____ Date _____

The following events were part of Roberto Clemente's life. Put them in the correct order by numbering them from 1 to 7. Write the number in the box.

Joined the Pittsburgh Pirates [ ]

[ ] Married Vera in Puerto Rico

Pedron Zarilla asks him to play on the Santurce Crabbers team [ ]

[ ] Signed with the Brooklyn Dodgers

Was born in Puerto Rico in 1934 [ ]

[ ] Died in a plane crash on the way to Nicaragua

Earned the most valuable player award [ ]

Exercise 1 Analysis   A Visit to the Clerk of the Weather

Name _____ Date _____

A. Compare the characters Spring and Jack Frost from the story.
Write about each one on the lines below.

SPRING

_____

_____

_____

_____

_____

_____

_____

_____

_____

_____

JACK FROST

_____

_____

_____

_____

_____

_____

_____

_____

_____

_____

B. Which is your favorite season Spring or Winter? Why?
Write about your favorite season in the space below.

_____

_____

_____

_____

_____

Exercise 2 Evaluation   A Visit to the Clerk of the Weather

Name _____ Date _____

A. In the story, the visitor from Boston learns that Spring has filed a lawsuit against Jack Frost. Pretend you are the lawyer for Spring. You are trying to persuade the jury that Spring should be allowed to visit Earth sooner. Jack Frost should not have such a long stay. First, there are some things you must do before you prepare your final argument. Ask yourself the following questions. Write your answers in the space below each question.

What are the advantages of Spring?

_____   _____

_____   _____

_____   _____

What are the disadvantages of Winter?

_____   _____

_____   _____

_____   _____

B. Now you are ready to prepare your argument which you will present to the jury. This is the time you must persuade, or make the jury believe that your reasons are good enough for you and your client to win the case. Here is your argument:

Argument: If the winter season is kept too long, people would suffer.

Write reasons to support your final argument in the space below. Refer to your questions and answers above as often as you feel it is necessary. If you need more space, use the back of this sheet.

_____

_____

_____

_____

_____

_____

Exercise 1 Analysis   The First Tornado

Name _____ Date _____

Circle *true* or *false* for each statement. If false, write the correct statement on the lines below.

1. The Medicine Man refused to help people.   TRUE   FALSE

_____

_____

_____

2. The Medicine Man formed a horse out of clay.   TRUE   FALSE

_____

_____

_____

3. The horse ran around town, kicking up wind.   TRUE   FALSE

_____

_____

_____

4. The people liked the wind.   TRUE   FALSE

_____

_____

_____

5. The rains came and filled the river.   TRUE   FALSE

_____

_____

_____

6. When terrible heat is followed by a tornado,
    the people know that rain will come.   TRUE   FALSE

_____

_____

_____

Exercise 1 Application   River Man

Name _____ Date _____

A. Think about the River Man's point of view.

Why is River Man disturbed when the men with modern ways come to the community?

_____

_____

_____

_____

_____

_____

_____

B. Think about the community's point of view.

1. Write the main events that led to the people using the river again.

_____

_____

_____

_____

_____

_____

2. Once the people begin to use the river again, what do you think they learn about life from River Man?

_____

_____

_____

_____

_____

_____

Exercise 1 Analysis   Winter Animals

Name _____ Date _____

Circle *true* or *false* for each statement. If false, write the correct statement on the lines below.

1. The author acted as if he were afraid of hounds.   TRUE   FALSE

    _____

    _____

    _____

2. The squirrels and mice fought for the narrator's supply of nuts.   TRUE   FALSE

    _____

    _____

    _____

3. The pine trees were alive and growing during the winter.   TRUE   FALSE

    _____

    _____

    _____

4. The author fed the rabbits potato parings.   TRUE   FALSE

    _____

    _____

    _____

5. The rabbits stood out against the color of the ground.   TRUE   FALSE

    _____

    _____

    _____

6. One rabbit was thin and bony.   TRUE   FALSE

    _____

    _____

    _____

Exercise 1 Application   Shipwreck of the Whaleship Essex

Name _____ Date _____

A. Pretend that you are the narrator. The captain has just returned. Write a paragraph below explaining to the captain what happened to the ship.

_____

_____

_____

_____

_____

_____

_____

_____

_____

_____

B. Now pretend you are the captain. Do you believe the story you just heard? Why or why not? Write in the space below.

_____

_____

_____

_____

_____

_____

_____

_____

_____

_____

Exercise 2 Synthesis   Shipwreck of the Whaleship Essex

Name _____ Date _____

In the story, the whalers live through the first, terrifying night at sea. What do you think happened the next day? Write an ending to the story in the space below.

_____

_____

_____

_____

_____

_____

_____

_____

_____

_____

_____

_____

_____

_____

_____

_____

_____

_____

_____

_____

_____

_____

Exercise 1 Synthesis   A Taste of Snow

Name _____ Date _____

A. Imagine that you are the narrator of the story and you are writing in your diary. It is the end of Christmas day, in the barracks of Manzanar. Write about what you did today and how you felt.

December 25

Dear Diary,

_____

_____

_____

_____

_____

_____

_____

_____

B. In each snowflake below, make a list of the narrator's memories of Christmas in Manzanar and Christmas in Ocean Park.

Christmas in Manzanar

Christmas in Ocean Park

C. What do you remember about holidays with your family? Write a list of your holiday memories on the back of this sheet.

Exercise 1 Application   **Winter**

Name _____ Date _____

A. In the poem "Winter," the poet explains how different animals and people
    prepare for the winter. List some ways that you prepare for winter.

    _____

    _____

    _____

    _____

    _____

    _____

B. Some people feel very unhappy during the winter season. As you prepare
    for the cold season, do you ever feel unusually sad? Why or why not?

    _____

    _____

    _____

    _____

    _____

C. How do you think the poet feels about the coming winter?

    _____

    _____

    _____

    _____

    _____

Exercise 1 Analysis   The Sky Is Low

Name _____ Date _____

A. Draw a line from each description in "The Sky is Low" to its meaning.

"The Clouds are mean."   It is howling or whistling.

"The Sky is low."   They are dark and threatening snow.

"A Narrow Wind complains all Day."   There are lots of these hanging
                                          overhead.

**B. How would you describe "Nature without her Diadem"? Write a brief
     paragraph in the space below.**

_____

_____

_____

_____

_____

_____

_____

_____

**C. Pretend you are a weather person for station XQV in Florida. Describe
     the weather report you will give your audience for a day when Nature
     is wearing her Diadem.**

_____

_____

_____

_____

_____

Exercise 1 Analysis

Birdfoot's Grampa

Name _____ Date _____

In this poem we learn that Birdfoot's Grampa cares about the toads. In the spaces below, list details that describe how Grampa feels.

Exercise 1 Synthesis

In Hardwood Groves

Name _____ Date _____

A. Robert Frost had a special talent for describing nature. In this poem, he explains the life cycle of the forest. Fill in the blanks to complete the cycle.

1. The leaves provide shade from the hot sun to the flowers and other plants.

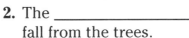

2. The _____ fall from the trees.

5. The rich soil helps _____ grow.

3. The leaves cover the _____ .

4. The leaves decay and provide nutrients to the _____ .

B. The cycles, or changes which happen in nature, are necessary to life on Earth. Can you think of other cycles that happen in nature? Use the back of this sheet to write a list.

Exercise 1 Application

Sierra

Name _____ Date _____

In the poem, the narrator is a mountain. The history of the mountain is told from the mountain's point of view. As the mountain tells the story, it mentions glaciers, wind, animals, and man. All played, or will play, a part in shaping the life of the mountain. In the space below, describe the mountain's story from these points of view. Use the word "I" in each answer.

1. Animals:

    Why is the mountain important for animals?

    _____

    _____

    _____

    _____

    _____

2. Nature (glaciers, wind, and sun):

    Describe how nature changed the mountain.

    _____

    _____

    _____

    _____

    _____

3. Man:
    What do you think man will do to the mountain?

    _____

    _____

    _____

    _____

    _____

Exercise 1 Analysis   Big Yellow Taxi

Name _____ Date _____

A. The author feels that the development of cities takes away from the beauty
of nature. Write examples from the poem that compare natural beauty
with construction and development. List them below. The first one has
been done for you.

NATURAL BEAUTY   CONSTRUCTION AND DEVELOPMENT

_____trees_____   _____pink hotel_____

_____   _____

_____   _____

_____   _____

_____   _____

_____   _____

_____   _____

B. What do you think is naturally beautiful? Write a paragraph describing
your idea in the space below.

_____

_____

_____

_____

_____

_____

_____

_____

_____

_____

_____

Exercise 1 Analysis   Narrative of the Life of Frederick Douglass

Name _____ Date _____

Circle *true* or *false* for each statement. If false, write the correct statement on the lines below.

1. Mr. Covey owned the slave who narrates the story.   TRUE   FALSE

    _____

    _____

    _____

2. The narrator's spirit was hard to break.   TRUE   FALSE

    _____

    _____

    _____

3. Master Thomas beat the slave until he was weak.   TRUE   FALSE

    _____

    _____

    _____

4. The narrator compared himself to boats on the Chesapeake.   TRUE   FALSE

    _____

    _____

    _____

5. The slave didn't fight back after he was pulled from the loft.   TRUE   FALSE

    _____

    _____

    _____

6. The narrator would never allow people to beat him again.   TRUE   FALSE

    _____

    _____

    _____

Exercise 2 Synthesis Narrative of the Life of Frederick Douglass

Name _____ Date _____

What do you already know about the history of slavery in America? What do you want to know more about? What have you learned from reading the story? Complete the chart by filling in the columns.

1. In the first column, fill in what you already know about the history of Africans who were enslaved in America.

2. In the second column, fill in what you want to know about the history of Africans who were enslaved in America.

3. After you have read the story, fill in the final column with what you have learned about the life of one man who was enslaved.

What Do I Know?	What Do I Want to Know?	What Have I Learned?
_____	_____	_____
_____	_____	_____
_____	_____	_____
_____	_____	_____
_____	_____	_____
_____	_____	_____
_____	_____	_____
_____	_____	_____
_____	_____	_____
_____	_____	_____
_____	_____	_____
_____	_____	_____
_____	_____	_____
_____	_____	_____

Exercise 1 Analysis   **Little Things Are Big**

Name _____ Date _____

Create a story map by filling in the boxes and blanks below.

TITLE: _____

SETTING:
Where does the story take place?

CHARACTERS:
Who are the main people in the story? _____

_____

PROBLEM:
What is the main problem in the
story that needs to be resolved?

EVENTS:
What are some of the
events that lead to solving
the problem? (HINT: These
can be thoughts or memo-
ries that a main character
has.)

EVENT 1: <u>The narrator thought the woman</u>
<u>might be prejudiced.</u>

EVENT 2: _____

_____

EVENT 3: _____

_____

SOLUTION:
How is the problem solved?

Exercise 2 Evaluation   Little Things Are Big

Name _____ Date _____

At the end of this story, the man did not help the woman, but he decided to help if something like that happened again.

In your opinion, was the man right for not helping the woman? Why? Write your decision below. Then list some reasons for your decision. The reasons can be from the story or from your own personal experiences.

The man was _____ when he did not help the woman.
                    (right/wrong)

My reasons are:

_____

_____

_____

_____

_____

_____

_____

_____

_____

_____

_____

_____

_____

_____

Exercise 1 Analysis   Chief Seattle's Oration

Name _____ Date _____

A. Match the phrases from *Chief Seattle's Oration*. Draw lines from each item in the first column to match the meaning in the other.

Big Chief at Washington   white settlers

forefathers   ancestors

Red Man   U.S. President

paleface brothers   Native Americans

B. How did Chief Seattle compare and contrast Native American and European American cultures? Discuss the different views about the world each culture has, as Chief Seattle describes it.

LAND:

Native American view:

_____

_____

European American view:

_____

_____

HONORING THE DEAD:

Native American view:

_____

_____

European American view:

_____

_____

Exercise 2 Synthesis   Chief Seattle's Oration

Name _____ Date _____

A. Below is an imaginary journal entry written by Chief Seattle. Fill in the spaces with words that you think he would have written.

Today, I must speak to _____. I must

speak about the traditions of the _____.

I feel _____ today. My people were

once _____ and _____.

Now, we must decide whether to live on the _____.

Why has the _____ forsaken us? The

_____ says he will protect us. If this is true, it is

_____ . But we must be allowed to honor our

_____ . Their traditions and dreams are our

heritage and we will never forget them. We will also never forget the beautiful

_____ we live in. The soil is _____

to us. The future looks _____ for our people.

B. How would you feel if you and your family were forced to leave your home and live in a strange place? Write in the space below or use a separate sheet of paper for your answer.

_____

_____

_____

_____

_____

_____

_____

Exercise 1 Evaluation

Ribbons

Name _____ Date _____

As you read the story, you will find that there are important relationships between characters. Describe the relationships between the characters listed below by answering the following questions.

What is the relationship between the two characters at the beginning of the story? Does an important change occur by the end of the story? If it does, why?

Stacy and her grandmother

_____

_____

_____

_____

_____

Stacy and her mother

_____

_____

_____

_____

_____

Stacy's mother and Paw-Paw

_____

_____

_____

_____

_____

Exercise 2   Analysis   Ribbons

Name _____ Date _____

A. The narrator of "Ribbons" became upset after grandmother began staying with her family. Put a check next to the reasons why the narrator was upset.

_____   Grandmother made her eat different foods.

_____   Grandmother paid attention to Ian.

_____   She was not allowed to watch her favorite TV shows.

_____   She was not allowed to read her favorite stories.

_____   She was not allowed to go to the dance class.

_____   She was forbidden to walk in the park with her friends.

_____   Grandmother was given her bedroom.

_____   Grandmother had stopped her from dancing with her toe shoes.

_____   Grandmother told her she was not pretty.

_____   She was not allowed to make noise in the house.

B. The grandmother has different traditions, actions, and beliefs from her grandchildren. Think of your own family. On a separate sheet of paper, compare your traditions, actions, and beliefs with an older family member. Are any the same? Are many different?

Exercise 1 Application   **Amigo Brothers**

Name _____ Date _____

When writing a story, an author develops a main idea. Supporting details are used to help the reader understand the main idea. Write the main idea of "Amigo Brothers" under the boxing ring below. Write supporting details in the remaining boxes.

MAIN IDEA

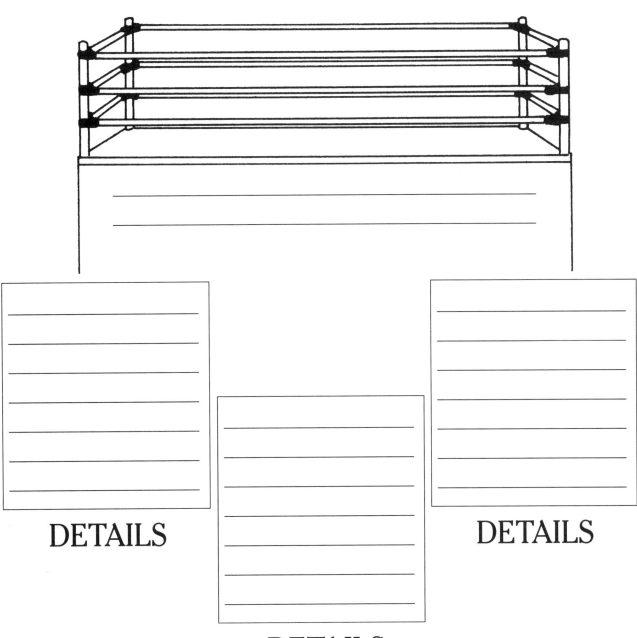

DETAILS

DETAILS

DETAILS

Exercise 2 Analysis   Amigo Brothers

Name _____ Date _____

Circle *true* or *false* for each statement. If false, write the correct statement on the lines below.

1. The boys ran along the Hudson River.   TRUE   FALSE

   _____

   _____

   _____

2. Antonio and Felix were brothers.   TRUE   FALSE

   _____

   _____

   _____

3. Both boys had won many fights.   TRUE   FALSE

   _____

   _____

   _____

4. Antonio and Felix wanted to fight each other.   TRUE   FALSE

   _____

   _____

   _____

5. The amigo brothers were not ashamed to hug each other. TRUE   FALSE

   _____

   _____

   _____

6. The boys stayed to find out who won the fight.   TRUE   FALSE

   _____

   _____

   _____

Exercise 1 Synthesis   **Ballad of Birmingham**

Name _____ Date _____

A. Put the events in the correct order by numbering them 1-6. The first one has been done for you.

____   Mother explains that there will be dangerous guns, clubs, and hoses at the march.

____   Mother hears explosion.

_1_   Daughter asks if she can join in the freedom march in Birmingham.

____   Mother suggests the child sing in the church choir.

____   Mother finds daughter's shoe in the rubble.

____   Daughter dresses up and goes to church.

B. Have you or someone you know ever experienced a tragedy? Write about it in the space below.

_____

_____

_____

_____

_____

_____

_____

_____

_____

_____

_____

Exercise 1 Application   Taught Me Purple

Name _____ Date _____

A. In this poem, colors represent feelings. How does each color make you feel? Write your answer for each color on the lines below.

purple   _____

gold   _____

blue   _____

red   _____

black   _____

green   _____

B. In "Taught Me Purple," the poet describes the colors of her world. Each color represents something different to her. What are the colors of your world? List them below.

_____   _____

_____   _____

_____   _____

_____   _____

C. Look at the colors you chose. What do you feel about your neighborhood when you see these colors? Write a brief description in the space below. If you need more writing space, use the back of this sheet.

_____

_____

_____

_____

_____

_____

Exercise 1 Synthesis   Simple-song

Name _____ Date _____

A. The poet discusses relationships, when they begin and when they end. What words and phrases does the poet use to describe the beginning of a relationship? What words are used to describe the end of a relationship? List the words and phrases below in the proper columns.

Beginning of a relationship   **End of a relationship**

_____   _____

_____   _____

_____   _____

_____   _____

_____   _____

_____   _____

B. You are an artist. You have been hired to draw a logo (a special symbol or design) for a club in your school. The logo should be a symbol which shows that all students in the club are working together to promote good relations in the school. Communication will be very important. Establishing good relationships will be very important.

Before you begin work on your logo, read the poem "Simple-song" again. What symbols are used in the poem that you might be able to use in your logo? Are there any ideas you can use from your list of words and phrases about relationships? Brainstorm some logo ideas. Use the space below. Then use the back of this sheet to draw your final version of the club logo.

Exercise 1 Analysis   War Is Kind

Name _____ Date _____

A. Below are three characters the author speaks about in his poem. In your own words, write what happened to each of their loved ones in the war.

maiden

_____

_____

_____

_____

babe

_____

_____

_____

_____

mother

_____

_____

_____

_____

B. Make a list of words you would use to describe war.

_____

_____

_____

_____

_____

_____

_____

_____

Exercise 1 Analysis   Childtimes

Name _____ Date _____

A. In the box, write the name of your favorite character from the story. Write words describing the character around the box.

_____

_____   _____

My Favorite Character:

_____

_____   _____

_____

B. Your list of words should describe the personality of your favorite character. Review your list. Then compare your favorite character to a friend or relative you really admire. How are they alike? How are they different? Write your description in the space below. Use the back of this sheet if you need more writing space.

_____

_____

_____

_____

_____

_____

Exercise 2 Synthesis   Childtimes

Name _____ Date _____

A. Pretend that you are the narrator of "Childtimes." On the lines below, write a paragraph about yourself. Use information from the story to complete your paragraph. Write in the first-person point of view.

_____

_____

_____

_____

_____

_____

_____

_____

_____

_____

B. Now write a paragraph about your own childhood.

_____

_____

_____

_____

_____

_____

_____

_____

_____

Exercise 1 Analysis

The Medicine Bag

Name _____ Date _____

A. On the lines below, compare how the narrator and his sister Cheryl feel about their grandfather.

Narrator

Cheryl

_____   _____

_____   _____

_____   _____

_____   _____

B. You are one of Martin's friends. You have just spent the afternoon with him and his grandfather. Describe your visit and your opinion of Martin's grandfather in the space below.

_____

_____

_____

_____

_____

_____

_____

_____

_____

_____

_____

_____

_____

_____

Exercise 2 Application   The Medicine Bag

Name _____ Date _____

Martin's grandfather gives him a very precious family treasure. When Martin has children, he will probably continue the tradition. He will probably pass the medicine bag on to his son.

Write a scene in which this takes place. Write the conversation you think might occur between Martin and his grandson during this special event. Continue your work on the back of this sheet if you need more writing space.

_____

_____

_____

_____

_____

_____

_____

_____

_____

_____

_____

_____

_____

_____

_____

_____

_____

_____

_____

Exercise 1 Synthesis   Abuela

Name _____ Date _____

**Read the statements below about the grandmother. What do you think these
statements tell us about her? Write your answers on the lines below.**

1. "My abuela begins her daily ritual with *"Santa Maria, madre de Dios...."*

   _____

   _____

   _____

   _____

2. Abuela takes good care of her plants and *yerbas*.

   _____

   _____

   _____

   _____

3. Abuela tells her granddaughter to drink a special tea to cure her stomachaches.

   _____

   _____

   _____

   _____

4. Abuela wants the narrator to remember her cures.

   _____

   _____

   _____

   _____

5. " *'Yo soy mexicana; tu mama es mexicana pero tú eres americana.'*
   [I am Mexican, your mother is Mexican, but you are American.]"

   _____

   _____

   _____

   _____

Exercise 2 Application   Abuela

Name _____ Date _____

A. **Here is a list of some common home remedies. What do you think each will cure?**

CHICKEN SOUP will cure:

_____

GARLIC will cure:

_____

The juice from the leaves of the ALOE PLANT will cure:

_____

B. **Every culture has its own home remedy. Think of some home remedies practiced by your family. Write them on the lines below.**

_____

_____

_____

_____

What home cure have you used?

_____

Did it work? Explain.

_____

_____

_____

Exercise 1 Application

I Ask My Mother to Sing

Name _____ Date _____

A. **The poet uses imagery, or pictures created by words, to help us see the things described in the poem. On the lines below, write the words the author uses to create images.**

_____

_____

_____

B. **You are a friend of the poet. You take a trip to China and you visit some of the places described in the poem. Using imagery, or words which will make your friend see the area, write a postcard telling about your visit.**

Exercise 1   Synthesis

Mother to Son

Name _____ Date _____

At the end of this poem, the narrator tells her son that she is still climbing the stairs. What other experiences might she have as she continues? Write your predictions on the steps. Try to use words like the author used.

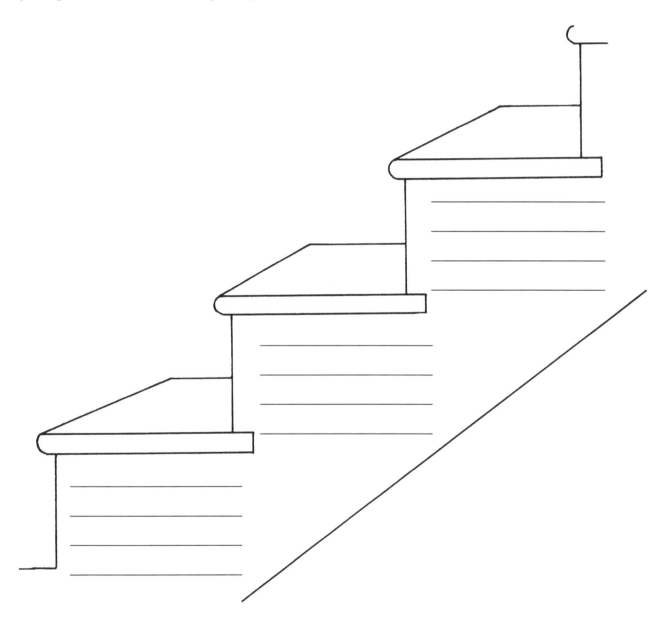

Exercise 1 Evaluation   My Father's Song

Name _____ Date _____

You are a poetry critic for the *Fearon Daily News*. Write a review of the poem "My Father's Song." First, give your readers a brief summary of the poem. Next, discuss reasons about why you did or did not like the poem. Finally, tell your readers if they should or should not read the poem.

FEARON DAILY NEWS

P O E T R Y   R E V I E W

My Father's Song by Simon J. Ortiz

_____   _____

_____   _____

_____   _____

_____   _____

_____   _____

_____   _____

_____   _____

_____   _____

_____   _____

_____   _____

_____   _____

_____   _____

_____   _____

_____   _____

_____   _____

_____   _____

Exercise 1 Evaluation   Lineage

Name _____ Date _____

A. In this lyric poem the author expresses how she feels about her
grandmothers. Fill in the blanks below to complete a description of how
you feel about one of your relatives.

My _____ is/was _____ .
   (relative)   (characteristic)

He/She _____ .
             (what your relative did)

He/She _____ .
       (how your relative displayed his or her characteristic)

My _____ is/was _____ .
   (relative)   (characteristic)

I am _____ .
           (one of your characteristics)

B. Write a story you might one day tell to your friends or children about one
of your relatives. Write the story as if you are actually speaking to those
who are listening.

_____

_____

_____

_____

_____

_____

_____

_____

Exercise 1 Application   Abuela

Name _____ Date _____

A. **The poet describes how her grandmother looks in great detail. On the lines below, list the words that the poet uses to describe the grandmother.**

_____

_____

_____

_____

_____

B. **What kind of portrait would you paint of the grandmother? Use your list of descriptions and your imagination to help you answer the following questions.**

1. Would you paint only her face or her entire body? Why?

_____

2. What color would you paint her eyes and hair?

_____

_____

3. Would you show her as a younger woman or as an elderly woman? Why?

_____

_____

4. What kind of expression would be on her face? Happy? Sad? Angry? Tired? Choose an answer. Why did you make that choice?

_____

_____

5. What would you paint in the background? Why?

_____

_____

Exercise 1 Synthesis   Grandma Ling

Name _____ Date _____

A. Pretend you are the author. Earlier today you arrived in Taiwan where you met your grandmother for the first time. How did you feel when you met her? What did the two of you talk about? Does she remind you of your father? Why or why not?

You are writing a letter to your father. Answer these questions in your letter to him. Use the space below to write your letter.

Dear Dad,

_____

_____

_____

_____

_____

_____

_____

_____

_____

_____

_____

_____

_____

Love,

_____

B. Write a short letter from Grandma Ling to her son. Describe how she felt when she saw her granddaughter for the first time in twenty years. How did Grandma Ling and her granddaughter spend their first day together? Use the back of this sheet to write your letter.

Exercise 2 Evaluation

Grandma Ling

Name _____ Date _____

A. When the narrator meets her grandmother, she says, "My image stood before me." What do you think the narrator means? Write your answer in the space below.

_____

_____

_____

_____

_____

_____

B. Think of your family. Is there someone in your family who you feel is your future image? Describe this person. In what way do you look like this person? Write your description.

_____

_____

_____

_____

_____

_____

C. Are there other ways in which you and this person are similar? Do you think the same way? In what way? Are the same things important to you? Describe what those things are. Do you walk, talk, or laugh the same way? Give a description of it. You don't have to answer all these questions. Answer one or two to help you start your paragraph. Use the back of this sheet if you need more writing space.

_____

_____

_____

Exercise 1 Synthesis   Aunt Sue's Stories

Name _____ Date _____

A. Put a check next to the stories that you think Aunt Sue would tell.

____   Story about World War II

____   Story about the Civil War

____   Story of the Underground Railroad

____   Story about President John F. Kennedy

____   Story about Sitting Bull

____   Story about an escaped slave

____   Story about the South

____   Story about becoming a free person

____   Story about slavery

____   Story about sadness and pain

B. If you were Aunt Sue, what kind of story would you tell? Brainstorm some ideas. Then write a title and your own story in the space below. Use the back of this sheet if you need more space.

TITLE: _____

_____

_____

_____

_____

_____

_____

_____

Exercise 1 Application   Bailando

Name _____ Date _____

A. **The title of this poem means "dancing." The author uses words in the poem to describe the feeling of dancing. List the words below.**

_____

_____

_____

_____

B. **How do you feel when you dance? In the space below, list words which describe the feeling.**

_____   _____

_____   _____

_____   _____

C. **In "Bailando" the poet describes a wonderful memory about a person she loves and respects. Is there a special memory you have about a person? Write about it in the space below. Use the back of this sheet if you need more writing space.**

_____

_____

_____

_____

_____

_____

_____

_____

_____

_____

Exercise 1 Evaluation   To My Dear and Loving Husband

Name _____ Date _____

A. The author has written a beautiful love poem to her husband. What do you think of the poem? Write a paragraph describing how you would feel if you received a poem like this from someone.

_____

_____

_____

_____

_____

_____

_____

_____

_____

_____

_____

B. If you were to write a poem to someone, whom would you send it to? What mood would it create: funny, sad, or romantic? What would it be about?

If I wrote a poem, I would send it to: _____
(person)

The poem would be: _____
(mood)

It would be about: _____
(theme)

C. Write your poem. Use the back of this sheet.

Exercise 1 Application

Escape: A Slave Narrative

Name _____ Date _____

Create a story map by answering the questions. Begin your answers at the "SETTING" mark.

CLIMAX

PLOT EVENTS
What happened to the
narrator when he came
upon the tavern?

_____

_____

_____

Why was it important for the
narrator to be at the tollgate?

_____

_____

_____

PLOT EVENTS
Why was the narrator heading
North?

_____

_____

_____

PLOT EVENTS
What did W.W. say to the narrator
after he asked for work?

_____

_____

_____

CHARACTERS
Who are the important people
in the story?

_____

_____

_____

END
At the end of the story, how did
the narrator remember W.W.'s
treatment of him?

_____

_____

_____

SETTING
Where does this story take
place?

_____

_____

_____

Exercise 2 Synthesis

Escape: A Slave Narrative

Name _____ Date _____

A. The story ends with the narrator thinking about the day that W.W. took him in. What will happen after he leaves the home of W.W.? Answer *yes* or *no* to the following questions. Then write what you think will happen.

Will he meet any other friendly people? _____

What will happen? _____

_____

Will he be recaptured? _____

What will happen? _____

_____

Will he see his family again? _____

What will happen? _____

_____

Will he be able to settle into a new life?_____

What will happen? _____

_____

B. The narrator decides he will not visit his brother on his journey North. If he had visited his brother, what do you think would have happened? Would his brother have let him go? Write your idea of the meeting in the space below.

_____

_____

_____

_____

_____

_____

_____

Exercise 1 Analysis

At Last I Kill a Buffalo

Name _____ Date _____

Circle *true* or *false* for each statement. If false, write the correct statement on the lines below.

1. Ota K'te's father was the Medicine Man of the tribe.   TRUE   FALSE

   _____
   _____
   _____

2. The narrator was excited about killing the buffalo.   TRUE   FALSE

   _____
   _____
   _____

3. The boy lied so that his father would be proud of him.   TRUE   FALSE

   _____
   _____
   _____

4. There was no yelling and shouting when the hunters
   attacked the buffalo herd.   TRUE   FALSE

   _____
   _____
   _____

5. The boy rode home on top of his kill.   TRUE   FALSE

   _____
   _____
   _____

6. The Chief gave the boy a new horse.   TRUE   FALSE

   _____
   _____
   _____

Exercise 2 Synthesis

At Last I Kill a Buffalo

Name _____ Date _____

A. Put the events in the correct order by numbering them from 1 to 6. Write the number in the box.

The boy gets his pony.

The father calls for his son.

The young buffalo falls.

The boy is lost in a cloud of dust.

The father gives away a horse.

The boy rides proudly back to camp.

B. Pretend that you are Ota K'te. It is the night after your first buffalo kill. Write the next sentence that describes how you feel.

Today I killed a buffalo. _____

_____

_____

_____

Exercise 1 Evaluation   The Secret Life of Walter Mitty

Name _____ Date _____

A. The story ends with Walter Mitty (in his imagination) facing a firing squad. Answer *yes* or *no* to the following questions. Then write what you think will happen.

Does he get shot? _____

What will happen? _____

_____

Does he escape? _____

What will happen? _____

_____

Does his wife return? _____

What will happen? _____

_____

B. Do you think Walter Mitty is crazy or just a day dreamer? Explain your answer on the lines below.

_____

_____

_____

_____

_____

_____

_____

_____

Exercise 2 Analysis   **The Secret Life of Walter Mitty**

Name _____ Date _____

The author does not tell us exactly who Walter Mitty really is or what his personality is like. However, we could make our own decision about what he is like from his actions.   Use the chart below to make a "word picture" of Walter Mitty.

In the box marked "Characteristic," write a word to describe Walter Mitty. Then, in the box marked "Example," write about a part of the story or write a quotation from the story to support your conclusions. The first one has been done for you.

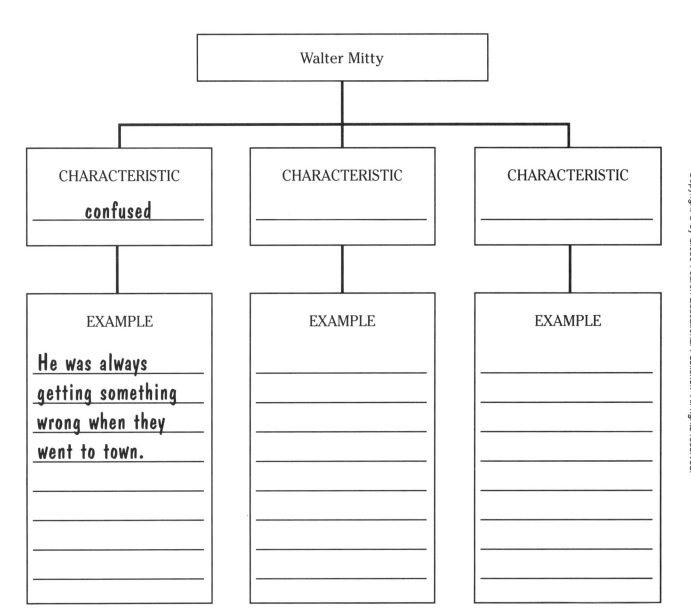

Walter Mitty

CHARACTERISTIC

confused

CHARACTERISTIC

_____

CHARACTERISTIC

_____

EXAMPLE

He was always
getting something
wrong when they
went to town.
_____
_____
_____
_____

EXAMPLE

_____
_____
_____
_____
_____
_____
_____

EXAMPLE

_____
_____
_____
_____
_____
_____
_____

Exercise 1 Analysis   The Invalid's Story

Name _____ Date _____

The following sentences describe the events of the story. Fill in the missing words. Use your answers to complete the puzzle.

ACROSS

1. The narrator's dearest boyhood _____ had died the day before the narrator returned home.

3. The narrator hurried to the railway station and found the _____.

4. Another man was also looking for a pine box, but his contained _____.

8. After trying many things, the expressman and the narrator decided they must remain _____ in the raging storm to get away from the odor.

DOWN

2. The friend had requested that the narrator take his _____ to Wisconsin.

5. The narrator didn't know it, but he had the _____ box.

6. A stranger placed Limburger _____ on the top of the box.

7. The narrator and the expressman thought the friend's body was causing the awful _____.

9. The men thought they had caught Typhoid _____ from the rotting corpse.

10. When the two men were taken from the platform, the narrator had a fever and predicted he would die soon. But he also found out that the smell was _____ caused by his friend's body, but by the Limburger cheese.

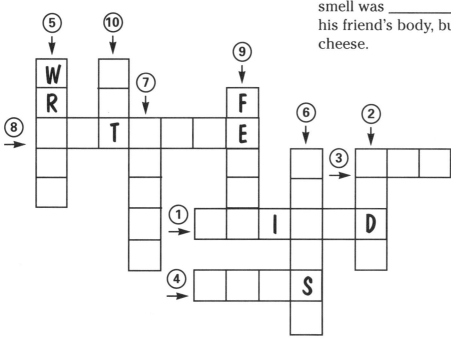

Exercise 2 Evaluation   The Invalid's Story

Name _____ Date _____

A. Decide whether or not you liked the ending of this story. Support your decision by checking off reasons from the list below.

I _____ like the ending of "The Invalid's Story" because:
      (did / did not)

_____ I like happy endings.   _____ I like scary stories.

_____ The men deserve their fate.   _____ I liked that the men were
                                                          dying at the end.

_____ The ending wasn't exciting.
                                                 _____ The story needed a sadder
_____ The ending needed more humor.   ending.

_____ I liked the characters.   _____ The ending wasn't complete.

_____ I didn't like that the men were dying   _____ The ending made me laugh.
          at the end.
                                                 _____ The ending made me sad.

B. If you didn't like the ending, select an ending from the list below that you might like better. If you liked the ending, pick an ending from the list that might be an appropriate second choice. You may also write your own ending on the last two lines.

_____ The cheese slides off of the box and into the expressman's lap before
          they resort to staying outside.

_____ The two men survive the cold and reach their destination in good health.

_____ The narrator and expressman open the box while riding the train.

_____ Inside the box, a gun explodes, killing the expressman and the narrator.

_____ The box really does contain a body and the cheese is not the cause of
          the smell.

_____ _____

          _____